CW00346290

DRASTIC FANTASTIC

Wise Publications
part of The Music Sales Group

London / New York / Paris / Sydney / Copenhagen / Berlin / Madrid / Tokyo

LITTLE FAVOURS

Words & Music by KT Tunstall

1. I___ slip soft - ly through
2. This si - lence sits eas - y, your___ so peace-

4

5

7

IF ONLY

Words & Music by KT Tunstall & James Hogarth

13

WHITE BIRD

Words & Music by KT Tunstall

with your face   so   pale._____

White bird,_   white bird_   with a black   tail.

FUNNYMAN

Words & Music by KT Tunstall & Martin Terefe

when I had to play your an - gel, sav-ing your soul?

E -ven through you were hold-ing on tight part of you was tak - en by your de-mons be- low.

And with no more to lose, you said you feel like a bruise

on a beau-ti -ful bod - y. And all the dam-age you do

HOLD ON

Words & Music by KT Tunstall & Edwin Makromallis

Say you___ to me,___ you're a bird with an eye for an-y-thing shin-y;___
Sim - plic - i - ty,___ a heart of gold, an old head on young shoul-ders;___

D.S. al Coda

31

HOPELESS

Words & Music by KT Tunstall

I DON'T WANT YOU NOW

Words & Music by KT Tunstall

41

42

SAVING MY FACE

Words & Music by KT Tunstall

all out of faith,___ I___ would give ev - 'ry - thing just for a taste.___ But ev - 'ry - thing's here,

1.

all out of place;___ los - ing my mem - o - ry, I'm los - ing the best of me. I'm all out of luck___

2.

- o - ry, sav - ing my_ face,___ sav - ing my_ face.___ (Oo.___ Oo.___

1-3. **4.**

Oo.)___ Oo,___ yeah.___ ___ yeah.___

SOMEDAY SOON

Words & Music by KT Tunstall, James Hogarth & Sam Dixon

51

⊕ *Coda*

E - ven though I know my way a - round,

pos - si - bly there's some - thing new I've found,

hold - ing on for find - ing sol - id ground Oh.

some - day soon.

BEAUTY OF UNCERTAINTY

Words & Music by KT Tunstall

1. I need a mir-ror and the eyes of a man.
2. Sit at my ta-ble, sip from my bowl.
3. Night is an ad-der, hid-den in grass;

I need no pro-tec- I feel like I know bites like her life

PAPER AEROPLANE

Words & Music by KT Tunstall

pres - sure's___ build - ing___ and some - thing has_____ to

give.

123456789

Exclusive distributors:

Music Sales Limited
14-15 Berners Street,
London W1T 3LJ, UK.

Music Sales Pty Limited
120 Rothschild Avenue, Rosebery,
NSW 2018, Australia.

Order No. AM992123
ISBN 978-1-84772-338-3
This book © Copyright 2007 by Wise Publications,
a division of Music Sales Limited.

Music arranged by Derek Jones & Jack Long.
Music processed by Paul Ewers Music Design.
Edited by Fiona Bolton.

Printed in the EU.